I Love that you're my Dad

ISBN-13: 978-1-56383-631-2
Item #4104

**Printed in the USA
by G&R Publishing Co.**

Distributed By:

507 Industrial Street
Waverly, IA 50677

www.cqbookstore.com

gifts@cqbookstore.com

 CQ Products

 CQ Products

 @cqproducts

 @cqproducts

This book is for my dad,

....

It's filled out with love by:

....

Given on this date:

....

One of my first memories of you...

When I think about our house growing up...

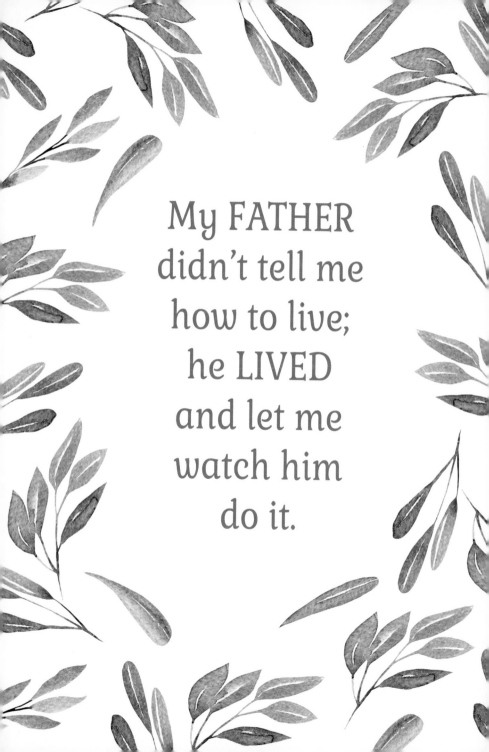

My FATHER
didn't tell me
how to live;
he LIVED
and let me
watch him
do it.

A typical family dinner at our
house consisted of...

I miss this most about
being a kid...

When I think about a typical day at home when I was young, you were...

The place my heart will always call home is...

_____

_____

_____

_____

_____

Your home now makes me think about...

_____

_____

_____

_____

My favorite game to play with you used to be...

_____

_____

_____

_____

_____

now it is...

_____

_____

_____

_____

_____

Growing up, spending time
with you meant...

_____

_____

_____

_____

The time we spend
together now...

_____

_____

_____

_____

Our shared adventures...

(Shade where you've visited together and notate where you've lived together.)

Others:

My favorite places
we visited are...

----

because...

Thank you for letting me...

I know I tested your
patience when...

_____

_____

_____

_____

Speaking of patience,
remember the time...

_____

_____

_____

_____

Remember how we always
used to fight about...

_____

_____

_____

_____

_____

but we always laughed about...

_____

_____

_____

_____

_____

_____

_____

Remember that time you grounded me for...

I definitely did / did not deserve it!
(choose)

The most memorable practical
joke you ever played on me...

_____

_____

_____

_____

The most memorable practical
joke I played on you...

_____

_____

_____

_____

Being a DAD
isn't a
big thing...
it's a
million
LITTLE things.

Long car rides for our family usually involved...

One of my biggest fears
as a child was...

This is how you
helped me with it...

Although I complained at
the time, thank you for making
me do these chores...

I secretly enjoyed this chore...

Thank you for the countless hours you spent...

I always loved hanging
out with you...

----

because...

Some things you and I enjoyed doing together...

You taught me the
importance of...

_____

_____

_____

_____

love
you
Dad

You used to always tell me to...

and I finally understand...

Remember the time I...

Thank you for putting
up with me when I...

_____

_____

_____

_____

I was always so
happy when you...

_____

_____

_____

_____

Behind every good KID is a great DAD

What we enjoy: (circle choice)

Me

comedy or drama

city or country

beach or mountains

tea or coffee

TV or radio

sweet or salty

morning or evening

dog or cat

movies or books

spring or fall

cake or pie

You

comedy or drama

city or country

beach or mountains

tea or coffee

TV or radio

sweet or salty

morning or evening

dog or cat

movies or books

spring or fall

cake or pie

I love to tease you about...

But to be fair, you
always tease me about...

It's the
LITTLE
memories
that will
last a
LIFETIME.

If you had a superpower, it would be...

because...

I think you're courageous because...

I SMILE
because you're my

I LAUGH
because there's nothing
you can do
ABOUT IT.

You passed along
these quirky habits...

Things I say now
that remind me of you...

You're my go-to expert on...

Something I still wish you would teach me...

Your hidden talents are...

if DAD can't FIX IT, no one CAN!

Some of the traits I
admire most about you...

I'm beginning to see
more of you in me...

I've inherited your...

One way I strive to be like you...

I love that we have
the same taste in...

memories
are
the greatest
inheritance
— peter hamill

If I could give you any gift, it would be...

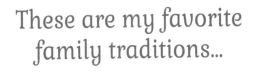

These are my favorite
family traditions...

Some of the
absolute
BEST THINGS
in life are
silly and
unnecessary.

One of the silliest things I
remember you doing...

....

....

....

....

One of the most unnecessary
things I remember you
doing for me...

....

....

....

As I navigate my life, I'm thankful that you...

I love that you love my...

_____

_____

_____

_____

I share your love of...

_____

_____

_____

_____

_____

_____

_____

You encouraged me to...

_____

_____

_____

_____

If it wasn't for you, I never would have...

_____

_____

_____

_____

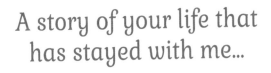

A story of your life that has stayed with me...

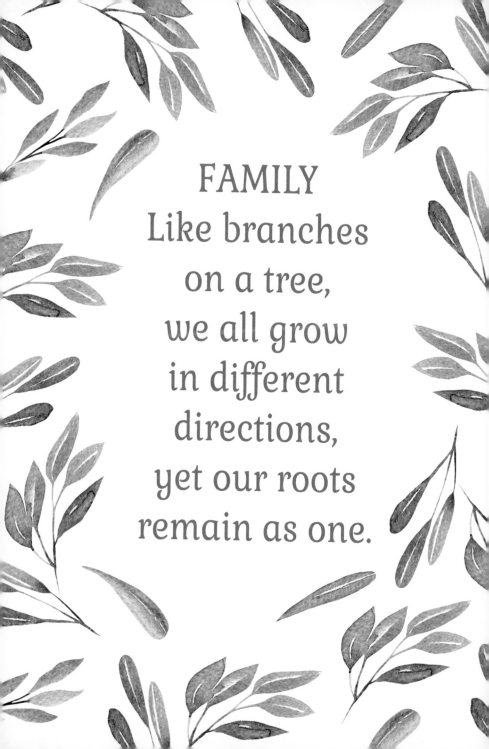

FAMILY
Like branches
on a tree,
we all grow
in different
directions,
yet our roots
remain as one.

I am proud of you for...

The world is a better place
because of your...

These are favorites that we have shared:

movie or TV show:

restaurant:

hobby:

sport:

meal:

holiday:

A song that always reminds me of you is...

because...

I laugh whenever I think about...

Your laugh makes me...

_____

_____

_____

_____

best
Dad
ever

If we traded places for a day,
my day would look like this...

_____

_____

_____

_____

and your day would be...

_____

_____

_____

_____

Something you tried to teach
me that didn't go so well...

_____

_____

_____

_____

_____

Our greatest
accomplishment together...

_____

_____

_____

_____

_____

I will cherish these memories forever...

Vacation:

Summer:

Holidays:

Birthdays:

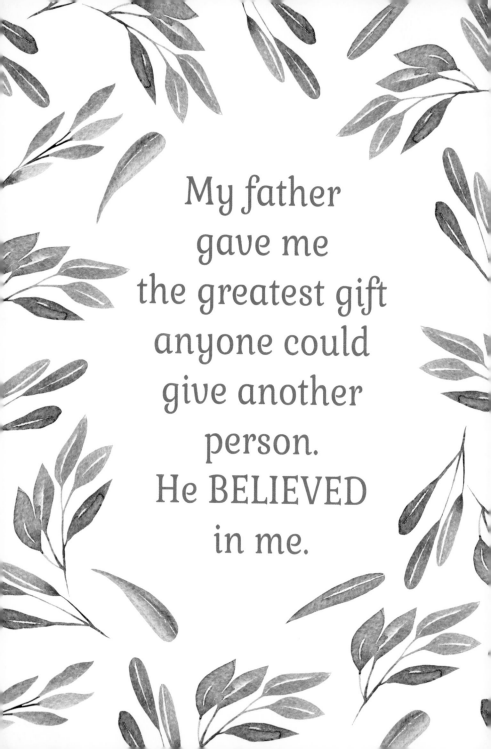

My father
gave me
the greatest gift
anyone could
give another
person.
He BELIEVED
in me.

Thank you for instilling
in me a love of...

and for teaching me
these life skills...

This is my favorite photo of us.

place photo here